WORKBOOK

For Use With

"I Will Give You Rest"

By Edward Kurath

A Journey of Recovering The Buried Treasure In Your Heart.

Workbook for I Will Give You Rest

Copyright © by Edward Kurath

Published by: Divinely Designed
P.O. Box 7501, Golden, Colorado 80403
www.divinelydesigned.com

ISBN 978-09764551-3-4
First printing 2014
Printed in the United States of America

Copyright Permission

The Content Questions were developed by Edward Kurath.

The "Application Questions" were developed in conjunction with Beth Shewchuk, MS, LPC, NCC. Beth is a Christian counselor in Spokane, Washington. She has taught seminars based upon "I Will Give You Rest." You may contact her at counselorshewchuk@gmail.com.

Feedback

As you work through this workbook, if you have any suggestions for improvement, please e- mail us at edkurath@divinelydesigned.com.

TABLE OF CONTENTS

Section 1: Book Study Aid

Chapter by chapter study and application

STUDY SUGGESTIONS

How Can Your Life Change?

The book "I Will Give You Rest" explains the provision Jesus made by which your life can be changed.

For this information to bring about change in your life, you need to **apply** it.

<u>How</u> Do You Apply It?

The content of the book is most potent if you are reflecting on your own life and experience as you study each chapter.

For most of us in our culture, studying the content of the book is more comfortable.

Applying the truths to your own life can be much more uncomfortable; but without it, your life won't change.

Because Content and Application are such different parts of this process, we are including questions to help you with both steps.

<u>Please be sure to read these instructions before you begin to answer the Book Study Aid questions (Section 1).</u>

There are **two** steps in your healing:

1. First, you need to **learn about** the provision God has made for you to enter His rest (read and study "I Will Give You Rest").
2. Then, you need to **apply** those provisions to your own life (pray about your own bitter roots, and thus be transformed into the image of Jesus).

The first step gives you a roadmap to where you are going.

The second step is actually taking the trip. **The second step** is more uncomfortable, is more work, is more time consuming, and therefore far more difficult. But your life will only change if you actually apply the blood of Jesus to the specific areas of need in your life.

So I would encourage you to do both steps if you want to experience the rest Jesus provided.

Accordingly, this the Book Study Aid portion has two sections for each book chapter:
1. **Content Questions**, and
2. **Application questions**.

The **Content Questions** are intended to help you learn about God's ways. After reading a chapter, <u>close the book</u> and try to answer the **Content Questions** for that chapter. Then open the book and go back and find the answers you missed.

The **Application Questions** are far more difficult, because they require you to be totally honest with yourself and the Lord, and they require you to enter into and explore the painful areas of your life. That is not fun. However, the goal is to then have the pain removed by Jesus.

Do not try to answer the **Application Questions** until after you feel confident of your answers to the **Content Questions**.

Life History Form

I have included a **Life History Form** in this Workbook (Section 6). I would highly recommend that you complete the **Life History Form** early in this process. The experience of reflecting on your life as you answer these questions about your life will help you to understand more clearly your own roots and areas of struggle. This insight will make answering the **Application Questions** most productive for your healing.

The best thing to do is to print out the pages of the Workbook which contain the **Life History Form**. Then fill out the Form by hand. Perhaps use a pencil, because you may want to change some of your answers as your awareness develops.

Also, do not share your answers on the Life History Form. Keeping your answers confidential will make it easier for you to be completely honest with yourself with what you write.

Answering The Application Questions

When processing the **Application Questions**, get a pad of paper and pencil and get quiet and comfortable. We did not provide spaces in the Book Study Aid for your answers, because we did not want to limit the space you have available for your answers. Save your answers that you write down to the **Application Questions**, because later chapters will sometimes refer you back to prior answers.

Eliminate distractions, because you need to be focused inside yourself. Ask the Lord to help you. He knows the problems clearly, and wants to help you to see for yourself.

Then simply write out your answers as they come to you. Do not worry about grammar or proper organization. Do not judge what you are writing. Just let the answers flow.

Chapter Sequence

If you are doing this process alone, or with just one other person, I would suggest that you read the chapters in the order they appear in the book.

If you are doing this process in a small group, you may want to use a different sequence. To more quickly bring the group members to a place where they can begin to pray for each other, **after Chapter 5 you might insert Chapter 11 and the assignment to listen to every negative emotion.** You will find this exercise in Section III of this Workbook. Then depending on how many sessions you plan to do, you might shuffle some of the later chapters around, or combine them.

Keep in mind that if you change the chapter sequence from that of the book, occasionally a term or concept may come up that was defined in a chapter you skipped. I do not think you will find that to be disruptive.

Sections 2 and 3 of this Workbook give you additional tools to use in your healing walk.

Now you are about to enter into the most exciting and rewarding journey of your life!

Chapter 1

Content Questions

1. There were <u>two</u> miraculous gifts Jesus provided for us. They are:

   a. _____ life (a one time event).

   b. A_____burden now (a lifetime process)

2. We all try to please God but fail. This is because we don't know _____.

3. Are you the only Christian who fails?

   a. Yes

   b. No

Application Questions

1. In what ways have you tried to be a "good Christian" and failed? Be as specific as possible.

2. As you have struggled with these failures, have you become discouraged and wondered if it is even possible to please God? Elaborate.

Chapter 2

Content Questions

1. As Christians, our common experience is: (hint: Romans 7:15)._____

   _____

2. There are three realms God created:

   a._____

   b._____

   c._____

3. All three realms are (circle one):

   a. Random

   b. Part of our fallen nature

   c. Orderly

   d. Unpredictable

   e. Mysterious

   f. Unknowable

4. As a scientific culture, we are all familiar with the _____ realm.

5. My will power has authority in the _____realm.

6. The Bible is our instruction manual for the _____realm.

7. My will power has no authority or power in the _____realm or the _____ realm.

8. In the spiritual realm, the operation of god's laws is like a speeding truck; and in comparison my will power is like an _____ on the highway.

9. God's spiritual laws are powerful, and they bring about _____ or _____.

10. We can stop the "speeding truck" by applying the _____ of Jesus.

11. Our _____ _____ has authority to stop bad behavior in the psychological realm.

12. The _____ of Jesus has authority to stop bad behavior in the _____ realm.

13. "Bad fruit" comes from "bad _____."

14. We can always tell there is a "bad _____" by the "bad fruit" in our life.

15. Both the "bad_____" and the "bad _____" are sin.

Application Questions

1. Keeping Romans 7:15 in mind, list those things that you don't want to do, but keep finding yourself doing anyway. Be specific.

2. Then list the good things that you would like to do, but somehow never are able to do. Again, be specific.

3. Have you sometimes had success in stopping "bad behavior" with your will power? If so, write about those successes.

4. Have you sometimes failed to be able to stop "bad behavior" with your will power? If so, describe these failures. Are these recurring patterns?

5. How have you <u>felt</u> when you have tried to stop the "bad behavior" problems in Question #2, <u>and failed</u>?

6. Are you surprised to know that God fully understands why you <u>must fail</u> in Question #2, and He is not condemning you, but rather wants to help you? (After all, God sent His Son to provide the only way for you to be successful in these situations).

Chapter 3

Content Questions

1. Love, joy peace, longsuffering, kindness, goodness are fruits of the _____. They are _____ fruit from a _____ root.

2. As a Christian, do you still have "bad fruit" in your life?
   a. Yes
   b. No

3. If "Yes", how can that be, since as a Christian you have been filled with the Holy Spirit?_____

   _____

4. The only way to end the "bad fruit" is to have the "bad roots" changed into the image of _____.

5. Jesus said, "Without Me you can do _____"

6. If we are transformed inside, we will be able to keep God's _____.

7. We never plant new "bad roots" after we become a Christian.
   a. True
   b. False

Application Questions

1. In the past, had you thought (or been taught) that as a Christian you should be able to <u>not sin</u>?
   a. Yes
   b. No

2. If your answer to Question #1 above was "no," skip to Question #3. If your answer was "yes," how did you feel whenever you did sin?

3. Do you personally know anyone who never sins? If so, list their first names.

4. Your "Honeycomb" (page 40) contains "bad roots" that produce the "bad fruit" in your life. How does it make you feel to have discovered there is a reason why you have patterns in your life that you have not been able to change, and that therefore there is hope for change? Elaborate.

Chapter 4

Content Questions

1. It is always a bad thing to judge.

    a. True

    b. False

2. There are four types of judging. Label them "good" or "bad".

    a. Judging by Jesus   _____

    b. I am the judge   _____

    c. Judicial authority of the church   _____

    d. My discernment   _____

3. Sinful (bad) judging brings _____.

4. If sinful judging is bad for you, why do you do it?

    _____

    _____.

5. If you have just "judged" something or someone, how can you tell if you have sinned or not?

    _____

    _____.

6. As human beings we _____ react to perceived wounding with bitterness, judgment, and blame.

Application Questions

1. Who has treated you unfairly in your lifetime? Make a list of them in order of how strongly you feel towards them.

2. Would it be difficult to let them "off the hook?"

3. Have you believed there was such a thing as "righteous anger" that it was OK for a Christian to indulge in? Elaborate.

4. Over the next week, make a list of things that do not go right for you. Then make a note as to who or what you judged at those moments.

5. In Question #4 above, did you frequently blame yourself?

Chapter 5

Content Questions

1. Forgiving and being forgiven is the only cure for _____.

2. The blood of Jesus stopping your reaping from sin is a _____.

3. List four things that forgiving is NOT:

    a. _____

    b. _____

    c. _____

    d. _____

4. Forgiving is releasing the other person to the judgment of _____.

5. Have you thought of your anger towards another person (your judging of them) as protection from future hurt?

    a. Yes

    b. No

6. If your answer to Question #5 is "Yes", are you aware that actually you are the one who suffers? Elaborate:

    _____

    _____

7. If you do not remove "bitter roots" immediately, which of the following happens:

    a.   They go away and don't bother you anymore.

    b. If you don't feel them, they have gone away.

    c. They get bigger and cause you bigger problems in the future.

    d. They remain dormant or stay the same.

8. Who do you need to forgive?

    a. Other people

    b. Yourself

    c. God

    d. Things

    e. All of the above

9. Forgiving needs to come from your _____.

10. In the process of forgiving, it is important to _____ words.

11. A rote prayer is important so that you are sure to say all the right words.

    a. True

    b. False

12. Though <u>entering into</u> forgiveness is a decision and not a feeling, when forgiveness has been <u>accomplished,</u> you feel the change.

    a. Yes

    b. No

Application Questions

1. Go back to your list of people who hurt you (Chapter 4, Question #1) and try forgiving them. If you initially need a format to use for praying, go to Endnote #5-4 for a sample prayer. You might start at the bottom of your list of people, because those people did not hurt you as severely, so it should be easier to forgive them. After you pray about a person, check and see if your feelings towards them have changed. If not, keep at it. Once you feel more peace, then work your way up the list to the next person.

2. Did you find it increasingly difficult to forgive as you moved up the list to the more hurtful people or circumstances?

3. If it was difficult or impossible to forgive some of the people as you worked your way up the list in Question #1 above, what might be holding you back is some misconceptions of what it means to forgive them. In this case, review page 63.

4. Was your name on the list that you were just praying through? In reflecting back, should it have been? If so, add your name to the list.

5. Was God's name on the list? Should it have been (Not because He did anything wrong, but because you judged Him)? If so, add Him to the list.

Chapter 6

Content Questions

1. God is a good Father, and He _____ you in many ways, though you man not be aware of it.

2. God does _____ afflict you, but He sometimes_____ let you experience difficulties, to motivate you.

3. The main purpose of your life is to

   _____

4. The only way you can act like Jesus is to _____ like Jesus.

5. Being "saved" has <u>two</u> meanings.
   a. Become His child (a one-time event).
   b. Be transformed into His _____ (an ongoing process).

6. God is personally directing every aspect of your life journey.
   a. True
   b. False

7. Whenever you encounter difficulties in your life, the correct question is: "Lord, what are you wanting to do in me through this trial?
   a. True
   b. False

8. The Christian life is a set of rules to keep.
   a. True
   b. False

9. If you think that your troubles are an attack of the Devil, you may find yourself interfering with God's_____ for your life.

Application Questions

1. Were things going well for you in your life when you decided to make Jesus your Lord, or were you struggling with difficulties? Describe:

2. Since you have been a Christian, has the Christian life felt like an easy yoke (Matthew 11:30), or a heavy burden?

3. When you try hard to keep "The List", what are you feeling:

4. Have you felt afraid, alone, abandoned, or overburdened in your Christian life? If so, describe this experience:

5. List two times when you felt as though God was against you. Describe the emotion you were feeling in those times.

6. Does it seem to be too good to be true that God is deeply committed to your protection and welfare? Elaborate:

7. Why is it so important for you to know that God has a good plan for your life? Use your own words:

Chapter 7

Content Questions

1. An Inner Vow is a _____ that you make, that contains the words _____ or _____.

2. Inner Vows are like a _____ track. They are inflexible and rigid.

3. The power behind an Inner Vow is the sin of _____.

4. New Years Resolutions are weak because they are made with your _____ power.

5. To stop the operation of an Inner Vow, first you need to deal with the sin of _____.

6. Sometimes people are afraid to renounce an Inner Vow, because they are afraid they will be like the person they _____.

7. "Good" Inner Vows also need to be renounced, because they are based upon _____ an bring bondage.

8. There are two ways of identifying the presence of an Inner Vow.

   a. Directly: recognize the rigid _____.

   b. Indirectly: when you have identified a _____ root judgment, look for a possible Inner Vow.

Application Questions

1. Write down any rigid behaviors in your life that you have been unable to change, no matter how hard you have tried (for example, angry outbursts, always being nice, never looking out for your own interests, etc.).

2. From the list in Question #1, can you write down an Inner Vow that fits each rigid behavior?

3. From the results of Question #2, can you identify a bitter root judgment that was being planted when you made each Inner Vow?

4. For those Inner Vows that you have just identified,

   a. Forgive and be forgiven for the bitter root judgment.

   b. Renounce the Inner Vow in the name of Jesus.

   c. Begin to observe whether the rigid behavior that had been a problem is gone, or diminished in strength.

Chapter 8

Content Questions

1. Would you say that you honor your patents? Describe:

   _____

   _____

   _____

2. There are _____ exceptions to the commandment to honor parents.

3. If you do not honor your parents, life will _____ go well for you.

4. Dishonoring parents is the same as judging them.

   a. True

   b. False

5. Honoring parents is:

   a. An obligation that is fulfilled when we forgive them.

   b. Is only necessary if they are "honorable."

   c. Is an ongoing future requirement.

   d. Is not a requirement that you have a future relationship with them.

6. Honoring parents means that you must not observe their negative attributes.

   a. True

   b. False

7. Honoring parents means that you have to allow them to treat you however they choose.

   a. True

   b. False

8. Honoring parents does not mean that they are valuable to you.

   a. True

   b. False

9. The nature of your relationship with your parents changes over _____.

10. When you are an adult, in order to honor your parents you need to obey them, like you did when you were a child in their home.

    a. True

    b. False

11. The way a person is to honor father and mother is the same for every set of parents.
    a. True
    b. False

12. You relationship with your parents has a subtle but profound effect on how you see _____.

Application Questions

1. What is your automatic "gut" reaction when you think of your parents?

2. Briefly describe each of your parents. Write down the first thoughts that come to your mind.

3. List some of the main strengths of your parents.

4. List some of the shortcomings of your parents.

5. Have their shortcomings substantially affected your relationship with them? If so, in what ways?

6. List specific ways where life has <u>not</u> gone well for you, where the troubles match the ways/areas that you have failed to honor your parents (for example finances, anger, infidelity, etc.).

7. List specific ways where life <u>has</u> gone well for you that match where you <u>have</u> been able to honor your parents.

8. Compare your experience of God with your experience with your parents. This is often a subtle, almost subconscious impression. Go deep. List the similarities (if any) or contrasts between how you see your patents and how you see God.

9. Based upon what you have just learned about what God meant when He told us to honor our father and mother, do you think you can honor your parents? If so, write down a plan as to how you can do that. If not, write down the obstacles to you being able to do that.

Chapter 9

Content Questions

1. The Lord created two places in us. What does the author call them?

   a. _____

   b. _____

2. Our conscious self is impacted by both the "World" and our _____ _____

3. When the message from our Treasure inside and the World are different, which one does the little child believe?

   a. Treasure Inside

   b. The World

4. A _____ begins to form when the dynamics in Question # 3 occurs.

5. The _____ not only separates us from our Treasure Inside, it also separates us from _____.

6. The Wall is made up of _____ and _____ _____ against <u>ourselves</u>!

7. We can remove The Wall by use of our will power. (by recognizing it is there and deciding to live differently).

   a. True

   b. False

8. Jesus told us to love our neighbor as ourselves. What part of ourselves do you think He was referring to? _____ _____.

9. When we hate ourselves, we experience the Big _____.

10. Addictions are ways people use to try not to feel the sensation of the Big _____.

Application Questions

1. If you treated other people the way you treat yourself, how many friends would you have?

2. Do you have any addictions or compulsive behaviors, or are you a people pleaser? Describe these issues.

3. If you try to refrain from the behaviors in Question #2 above, describe the feeling you experience.

4. How successful are you in refraining from the behaviors in Question #2?

5. Have you experienced rejection from someone you loved deeply? If so, how did that feel?

6. On a scale of 1 to 10, 10 being optimum, do you feel the presence of God, and can you hear His voice? Elaborate.

7. Do you feel as though there is a part of you that is so good that it is in the image of God? Elaborate.

8. Write an honest note/letter of forgiveness and appreciation to yourself. If you are not a "writer," speak it verbally.

Chapter 10

Content Questions

1. The worst trauma one can experience is the absence of the _____.

2. As a child, when we do not receive the "good" that we need, we judge

   _____.

3. As a child, when our legitimate needs are not met, we feel _____.

4. To deal with the feelings in Question #3, we build The _____.

5. The reason that we are not aware of the pain the "absence of the good" produced in us as a child is that we have built The _____ to not have to feel it.

Application Questions

1. How does it feel when someone gives you a hug?.

2. Do you feel uncomfortable when someone gives you a compliment?

3. Refer to the list of what we all need on pages 167-168 (pages 165-166 in 2005 printing). On a scale of 0 to 10, 10 being the most, how much of the "good" did you receive from your parents?

   a. Meaningful touch: Father _____   Mother _____

   b. Spoken words: Father _____   Mother _____

   c. High value   Father _____   Mother _____

   d. Special future   Father _____   Mother _____

   e. Active commitment   Father _____   Mother _____

4. Total up the numbers in Question #3 above.

   Total for Father   _____

   Total for Mother   _____

   Grand Total   _____

   The Grand total will be between 0 and 100. The further your Grand Total is below 100, the greater was your wounding from the Lack of the Good..

Chapter 11

Content Questions

1. Our emotions became corrupted at The Fall in the Garden of Eden, and therefore they now tend to lead us into sin.
   a. True
   b. False

2. Our physical sensations tell us about what is going on in our physical _____. Similarly, our _____ tell us what is going on in our psychological/spiritual self.

3. Emotions are _____ percent reliable about telling us what is going on inside us.

4. When we experience a negative emotion, we have to find a way to bring _____ inside us.

5. It is not selfish to have our legitimate _____ met.

6. Our emotions give us important _____ about our needs.

7. When our legitimate needs have been met, the emotional _____ stops.

8. Is the emotion of anger a sin?
   a. Yes
   b. No

9. I become "selfish" (hyper focused on myself) when my legitimate needs are not met.
   a. True
   b. False

10. Positive emotions tell us about good things going on inside us.
    a. True
    b. False

11. We need to learn the _____ of our emotions.

12. If we listen to every _____ emotion, the Lord can use that to guide us in our walk of healing.

Application Questions

1. What was the attitude towards emotions in your family of origin?

2. Have you believed/been taught that emotions are a problem (random, unpredictable, unreliable, lead you into sin)? Elaborate.

3. Think about a time when someone who was important to you abandoned or betrayed you. Name the feeling. _____.

4. Have you considered that you might have made an Inner Vow not to feel? Elaborate.

5. Enter into the following process:

   a. Think about a person who recently hurt you, or with whom you are angry.

   b. Feel the feeling.

   c. Forgive them, and ask the Lord to forgive you for judging them (Chapter 5). Ask Him to remove the bitter root, and invite Him into that place where the bitter root had been residing.

   d. Think about that person again, and feel the feeling.

   e. Name the new feeling. _____.

6. Begin to apply the exercise to listen to every negative emotion contained on pages 186-188 (this is not in the 2005 printing of the book). To get the exercise, go to www.divinelydesigned.com, click on 'Free Workbook" at the top of the home page. Print out the exercise "Listen To Every Negative Emotion." If you do not use the internet, contact us and we will send you a copy).

Chapter 12

Content Questions

1. Being humble means that you realize that you are fallen and not worth much.
   a. True
   b. False

2. We see ourselves as "worms," because that is what we are.
   a. True
   b. False

3. God doesn't understand how bad you are.
   a. True
   b. False

4. There exists in you a part of you that is made in _____ image.

Application Questions

1. Are you a bit shocked to discover that part of you is good? Elaborate.

2. What voices/influences have given you messages that you are worthless? List them.

3. Can you now understand that when Jesus told us to love ourselves, that He meant to love the part of us made in God's image (our Treasure Inside)? Elaborate.

4. Jesus said to love yourself (Matthew 22:39). If you have not been loving your Treasure Inside, can you now see why there is pain inside you and why life has not been going well for you? Elaborate.

5. Can you think of practical ways of how you can actually begin to love yourself? (hint: begin to listen inside as outlined in Chapter 11)? Write down your plan of action to actually love yourself.

Chapter 13

Content Questions

1. "Flesh" is always bad.
    a. True
    b. False
2. The "bad part" refers to three possibilities:
    a. Sensuality and lawlessness.
    b. Our tendency to judge.
    c. Trying hard to _____ _____.
3. The essence of the "bad part" can be referred to as the "primal sin," the desire to take _____'s place.
4. The "bad part" impels me to build The _____.
5. Our error tends to be to judge everything inside us as _____.
6. Name the tree places inside us that are below our level of consciousness.
    a. _____
    b. _____
    c. _____
7. "Die to self" means that we throw the baby out with the bath water.
    a. True
    b. False
8. Legalism is based upon the "bad part" of us.
    a. True
    b. False

Application Questions

1. When you misbehaved as a child, or was not able to be "good" as your parents wanted you to be, did you judge yourself as "all bad?"
2. Have you believed that "flesh" is always bad? Elaborate.

3. Have you been aware that trying to be good in your own strength is not only futile, <u>it is sin</u>? Elaborate.

4. Can you now clearly see why "legalism, " keeping the commandments by your will power, brings death instead of life? Elaborate.

5. Write down some specific times when you have tried very hard to please God, and failed.

6. Spend some time with your Treasure Inside (as best you can) and apologize for judging him/her as the problem, and ask the Lord to forgive you for judging yourself.

7. Memorize the diagram on page 204 (page 200 in the 2005 printing). Go back to it whenever you have condemned yourself. This diagram presents a new reality for most of us. You have probably spent your life condemning yourself when you made a mistake or sinned. And tragically, we all tend to condemn our whole self, not just the part that sinned. In order to love ourselves, we need to be fully convinced that there is a part of us that is not sinful – our Treasure Inside. If you are still unsure of this, restudy Chapter 12, and the Endnotes associated with it. The Endnotes contain detailed scriptural evidence for the presence of the Image of God in you.

Chapter 14

Content Questions

1. You are built for _____.

2. God is _____.

3. When you experience the presence of Jesus, you receive His _____.

4. The _____ interferes with your ability to experience Jesus' presence.

5. The journey towards experiencing Jesus' presence involves removing The _____.

6. The Lord would rather spend time with some special people, and not others.
   a. True
   b. False

Application Questions

1. How have you experienced God's love in the past?

2. Are you able to sense God's presence sometimes? Elaborate.

3. Does it seem like an impossible dream for you to have a close walk with the Lord?

4. As you continue to become your own friend, keep listening for His voice. As The Wall gradually comes down, you will hear Him more and more clearly. You can do it!

Chapter 16

Content Questions

1. Demons can be present in a Christian.
   a. Yes
   b. No
2. The "honeycomb" (page 40) illustrates how parts of us are filled with Jesus, but other parts of us contain _____ roots.
3. The Enemy and his demons have a legal right to oppress us through our _____ roots.
4. When you have troubles in your life, it is likely an attack of the Enemy. The best way to handle it is: in the name of Jesus, to rebuke Satan and the demons doing the work and to command them to leave you alone.
   a. True
   b. False
5. God protects His children and limits the damage that the Enemy can do to a Christian.
   a. Yes
   b. No
6. To get rid of a demon, first we cast them out so we can then bring healing to that place.
   a. True
   b. False

Application Questions

1. When bad things happen in your life, do you assume it is caused by Satan and/or demons?
   a. Yes
   b. No

2. If you answered "no", skip to Question #3 below. If "yes," answer this: If you really knew that God was next to you at the moment the bad thing happened, would you feel the same way? Elaborate.

3. If you were aware that the one standing next to you in the bad time was your parent, how would you feel at that moment, and explain why you think you would feel that way?

4. What might it take for you to accept that God is on your side and is protecting you (hint – it relates to your parents)?

Chapter 17

Content Questions

1. The path outlined in this book is a <u>totally</u> new way of _____.

2. You only need to walk this way in major crises. Otherwise, you can just go back to living life the way you always have.
   a. True
   b. False

3. _____ is actively directing your life, all day, every day.

4. If you do not continue to live in this new way every day, you will plant new roots of _____, and you will fall back into your old ways.

5. The new way is simple, but it is not always easy.
   a. True
   b. False

6. Other _____can help make your journey more successful.

Application Questions

1. In the past, have you been under the impression that if you could just get the right person to pray for you, your problems would be gone? If so, elaborate.

2. Was it a surprise to you to discover that your healing is a daily journey, not a one-time event? Elaborate.

3. If this new way of living seems overwhelmlingly difficult, consider whether there is fear or a strong negative emotion at the root of it. Trace the root of this emotion down into specific statements, for example: "The pain will never end," "I feel helpless and alone in life," "It is too hard," "Nothing else has ever worked," etc.

4. Use the steps in the <u>exercise to listen to every negative emotion</u> to help you on your journey (go to www.divinelydesigned.com. Click on "Free Workbook," and print out the exercise. In this way, you can let Jesus take you by the hand and lead you daily.

5. Try to find another same sex supportive Christian. Agree to meet together regularly to help each other continue on this healing journey, because having such support makes the daily journey easier.

Chapter 18

Content Questions

1. _____ yourself is an essential part of having life go well for you.

2. A truce in the war with yourself is the goal.

   a. True

   b. False

3. Giving yourself the _____ is a way of loving yourself.

Application Questions

1. Listen to your internal "self-talk" and discover what specific areas of your Treasure Inside you can quit stepping on, and start loving to life.

2. Think of two things you would do for your best friend, and do those for yourself this week.

3. Spend some quiet time this week focused on God's love for you and soaking in His presence.

4. If you are not sure what "love" is, read pages 394-399. This article is not in the 2005 printing. To read it, go to www.divinelydesigned.com. On the left side of the home page, click on "Articles." The article "What Is Love?" is listed there.

Section 2

Forgiving Produces A Miracle !

Forgiving is indeed miraculous. Doing so will activate the provision Jesus made for your life to change. Let me give you an example from my own life.

I am a jogger, and I live on the side of a mountain. In the winter it is icy, and I can't run here; because I will fall and break something. Therefore I drive 4 miles to town. There is a street that is about 1 1/2 miles out and 1 1/2 miles back that is plowed and sanded and does not have much traffic. That is my running track in the winter.

One day a few years ago I was almost at the far end of the run when two mid-sized dogs ran out after me. I have learned that you don't run from dogs, so I turned on them and I shouted,

"Hey, you get back there."

They skidded to a stop. The owner was a woman who was standing on the sidewalk.

She said, "Hey, don't talk to my dogs like that."

I said, "Lady, you have to be kidding me. We are in town, there is a leash law here. Your dogs shouldn't be here in the street."

She called her dogs and went inside.

As I continued my run, I was very upset.

I thought, "This is the only convenient place I have to run, and I'm not going to let those dogs spoil that. What will I do about it? I know what. I have a foot long steel bar in my garage. I'll carry that. Then when they come out, I'll take care of them."

Then I thought again. It wasn't really the dogs' fault, and I'd probably get in trouble if I hurt them. Then what can I do instead?

"I know what I'll do," I thought. "I'll carry my cell phone. Then when they come out after me, I'll grab one of them by the collar and call the dog warden. Then she'll get a ticket, and that should fix her."

I finished my run, drove home, took a shower, and went to my office. As I sat down, I was still chewing over this situation. As I grumbled over it, I got the distinct impression that the Lord was tapping me on the shoulder. I knew what He wanted: **He wanted me to forgive the woman**. I didn't want to forgive her, and argued with the Lord.

"But she was so thoughtless. She had no right to let her dogs loose, etc, etc, etc."

Eventually I realized I was going to lose the argument. I reluctantly agreed to forgive her, though I still didn't want to. After all, I still believed I was right, and she was wrong.

Initially as I prayed it was pretty mechanical and wooden. However, as I prayed, I gradually calmed down; and the forgiveness became more real.

- I forgave her.

- I asked the Lord to forgive me for judging her.

- I asked Him to take out the bitter root I had just planted,

- To cleanse that place, and

- To fill it with His Holy Spirit.

As I prayed, I began to recognize that she had a permanent scowl on her face. It also occurred to me that a healthy person would have said something like,

"I'm sorry, sir. Are you alright? Did my dogs scare you?"

I realized that she was a wounded and unhappy person. I felt compassion for her, and I began to pray for her. I suspected that she might not know the Lord, and I began to pray for her salvation.

Suddenly it was as though I was struck by lightning. The change in my mindset was stark. I realized that I was now seeing her the way the Lord sees her. I wasn't praying for her salvation because it was the "Christian thing to do." I was praying for her because I saw her pain and neediness.

I realized that a miracle had occurred!

Before I prayed, I was in a mindset of bitterness. I was on the throne, and in that mindset I was fully convinced that she was wrong, and I was sure I was right. I was in the mind of the "flesh." Bad fruit (my plans to make her pay) was coming from that bad root.

After I prayed, I saw her neediness and wounding. I was now seeing her as Christ saw her. I now had the mind of Christ. Jesus was now in me where the bitter root had previously been planted, and that new good root was producing good fruit (my compassion for her). I wasn't <u>trying</u> to see her with eyes of compassion. I simply did.

When **we forgive** and **Jesus forgives us**, a miracle occurs. It is not something we can accomplish on our own. We can repress our anger, or try to be nice; but we can't change what is inside us. Only the blood of Jesus can accomplish that change. And He does it! He came and died, rose again, and gave us His Spirit to make this possible!

Details of How to Forgive

If you are not yet convinced that forgiving is the only way to enter into the rest provided by Christ, then again read Chapters 2, 3, 4, and 5 in "I Will Give You Rest."

The Power Behind Forgiveness

When we judge, we have responded to our God-wannabe ("flesh"). We have then invited darkness into a place in us. When we forgive, we are getting off the throne as the judge; and we are inviting Jesus into that place. Jesus then comes in, as He has promised. He has the ability to come in and overwhelm the work that the Devil had done in us, because Jesus is more powerful than the Devil (1 John 4:4). If He were not more powerful, then we would be wasting our breath.

Once you are convinced, that **forgiving** and **being forgiven** by Jesus is so important, then the next important question is, **"How do I do it?"**

Forgive From The Heart

The key is that forgiving must come from the heart. It must be real. Because of this, reciting a rote prayer can be a mistake. We may come to rely on the words said and not on the heart change required. This is a real temptation, because reciting words is much easier than truly letting go of the resentment.

At the same time, it is sometimes helpful in the beginning to have some guidance of what to say. Therefore I somewhat reluctantly am providing several sample prayers. From the variety of samples, you can see that there is no magical set of words to speak, although you do need to actually speak words to accomplish forgiveness (though if others are present, sometimes it would be most appropriate to say it under your breath).

One way to keep from getting into the rut of a rote prayer is to use a different sample prayer each time. That way you may not get hooked on the exact words, but will begin to grasp the principles involved. Know that the goal is for you to be weaned from all sample prayers, and to just speak to the Lord spontaneously.

The Basics

One way to keep focused on the principles and not specific words is to keep in mind what forgiveness is, and why we need it.

The basic truth behind forgiving is that when we judge, we have taken Jesus' place on the throne as the judge. We are <u>never</u> authorized to judge anyone or anything, even if they are in fact guilty. This judging is sin; and to get free from the consequences of this sin, we need to forgive so that we will be forgiven. When we forgive, we are stepping down off the throne, and are inviting Jesus to take that place. We are asking Jesus to take out the bitter root we just planted in our "honeycomb" (Chapter 3), and to fill that place with His presence. In this way, since Jesus will now reside there, we are actually changed into the image of Jesus in that place in us. If you are unclear about this, reread Chapters 4 and 5.

When **we forgive** and **are forgiven by God**, the spiritual work has been done. However, if in judging we have done something to damage our relationship with the one we judged, we also need to repair that breach by approaching that one, acknowledging our sin towards them, repenting and asking them to forgive us.

Who Do We Judge?
Those that we judge include:
- Other people
- Things (inanimate objects)
- God
- Ourselves

Forgiving Other People and Things
People are capable of sinning, so praying to forgive them makes sense to us. Even though "things" are not actually capable of sinning, I find it easy to recognize that I do frequently accuse "things" of doing me wrong. Consequently it doesn't seem particularly strange for me to forgive my computer for being too slow, or my car for not starting.

Sample Prayers for Forgiving Others and "Things"
Note that in each case I would speak directly to the other person/thing, using the second person "you," as though he/she/it was present. This makes it more personal, and brings the event back to my mind. Usually I will not need to actually go to the one I judged and speak these words to them. The problem isn't in them, it is inside me.

Alternate #1
A prayer regarding your Dad might go something like this:

"Father God, I come to You in the blessed name of Jesus.
I realize that I have judged my Dad, and I have inside me a root of
        bitterness.
I am sorry that I did this, and I don't want that awful thing in me anymore.
Dad, I forgive you for _____ (the offense).
Lord, I ask You to forgive me for this judgment of bitterness.
Forgive me for taking Your place as the judge.
I ask You to come into that place in me, remove that ugly root from me,
        and wash me clean with Your blood.
Cleanse me in every place where that bitterness existed.
I ask You to fill all those places with Your presence.
Lord, I ask that You would bless my Dad. Amen."

Alternate #2

A prayer regarding Mom might go something like this:

> "Mom, I forgive you for _____. You owe me nothing – no restitution, no apologies, no explanation, no reasons, no excuses. I release you totally. I accept Jesus, as the restitution for your sin against me.
>
> Father, Your Word says, that If we confess our sins, we can trust you to be merciful and just and to forgive us of all unrighteousness. I have now confessed my sin, and know that You have forgiven me. As far as the east is from the west, you have put my sin from me, and You remember it no more."

Alternate #3

For example, a man cuts me off in traffic. I feel anger spring up in me. I honk my horn and utter some words. Then I would catch myself and say something like:

> "Lord, I have just judged that man." I would name the feeling behind the anger, in this case perhaps "demeaned", or "belittled."
>
> "Mister, I forgive you for pulling out in front of me, for treating me as being of less importance than you, for ignoring my safety.
>
> Lord, forgive me for judging that man, for taking Your place on the throne as the judge.
>
> I ask You to reach down inside me and remove that bitter root I just planted.
>
> Wash that place clean with Your blood, and then please fill that place with Your Holy Spirit.
>
> Lord, bless that man's day, and keep him safe.
>
> I pray this in the name of Jesus. Amen."

Alternate #4

This is an example based upon the Elements Involved in Forgiving on Page 69 of "I Will Give You Rest."

Example: I discover that my wife (Kay) has failed to do the laundry (we have agreed on who does which home chores, and this is one of hers), and I have no clean socks. I am angry at her, and say to myself: "There, she did it again!"

I have just planted a root of bitterness in myself, and I need the Lord to remove it.

Recognition: "I have just judged Kay for not having done the laundry."

Confession: "I sinned when I judged her."

Repentance: "I am unhappy that I did this, and want that bitter root taken out."

Forgiveness: "Kay, I forgive you for not doing the laundry, and leaving me without any clean socks."

Accept Forgiveness: "Lord, forgive me for judging Kay. Take out that bitter root I just planted. Cleanse that place with your blood."

Ask the Lord to Fill me: "Lord, I invite you to come into that place where the bitter root had been; and fill it with your Spirit."

Bless the other: "Lord, I ask that you would bless her in her busy schedule."

Restoring the relationship (Restitution): In this example, my wife was not present when I discovered that I had no clean socks.

If she had been present, and if I had spoken those angry words to her or otherwise acted angrily towards her, I would then need to restore our relationship. I would confess my sin against her, tell her how sorry I am that I hurt her, and ask her to forgive me for judging her, and wounding her. I might then agree to do something for her, like doing the laundry next week as a way of showing her that I really was sorry.

This is not legalism or "penance," because my agreeing to do the laundry is to restore my relationship with her, **not** as a way to wash away my sin. That had already been taken care of by the blood of Jesus.

Forgiving God

God is incapable of sinning. Intuitively we know this, so to say to God "I forgive You" somehow feels awkward and not genuine. At the same time, we have in fact sinned by judging Him; and to remove that sin, we need to forgive so we can be forgiven. We also need to restore the relationship.

Using different words that parallel the meaning of "forgive" should remove this awkwardness. For example:

> "<u>God</u>, I wrongly judged You as ____(name the judgment)____ . My God wannabe ("flesh") lied to me about You. I release You from the debt I charged against You. I know that You did not ____(name the judgment).____ Lord, I ask that You release me from the debt that I owe for having taken Your place as the judge of You. I ask You to take out the bitter root, and wash me clean with Your blood. Please come into that place, filling that place in me with Your Holy Spirit."
>
> Lord, I am so sorry that I judged You. Please forgive me."

Forgiving Yourself

Keep in mind that judging yourself causes many of the most hurtful feelings that a person experiences. The most common such difficulties include anxiety, people pleasing, depression, and outbursts of anger. The self-judgments need to be healed by forgiving and being forgiven by Jesus, just as do all other bitter root judgments.

Judging ourselves is also very common, and very destructive to us. Forgiving ourselves is more complex than forgiving God, because our "flesh" (God-wannabe, Chapter 13) is capable of sinning; and yet our Treasure Inside (Chapters 9 and 12) is made in God's image, and therefore does not sin. Whenever we judge ourselves, we always condemn both our God-wannabe and our Treasure Inside. Therefore, not only is this judging a sin, it is an affront to our Treasure Inside.

Because our Treasure Inside is not capable of sinning, "forgiving" ourselves may seem awkward. As with forgiving God, using different words that parallel the meaning of "forgive" should remove this awkwardness. And of course, we want to restore our relationship with our Treasure Inside. For example, focus your attention inside and speak to your Treasure Inside:

Example #1:

"_____(speaking to your own Treasure Inside), I wounded you by accusing you as being _____ (the judgment of yourself). I feel your pain, and I am sorry for having judged you in that way. My God-wannabe lied to me about you, and I believed that lie. I release you from the debt that I charged against you, and I ask you to forgive me for hurting you in this way.

Lord Jesus, I ask you to forgive me for having judged myself. I ask you to take out this bitter root, to cleanse that place with Your blood, and I invite you to come and fill that place with your presence."

Example #2

"_____(speaking to your Treasure Inside), I wrongly judged you as being _____ (the judgment of yourself). My God wannabe lied to me about you. I release you from the debt I charged against you. I know that is not true of you. I am so sorry that I judged you. Please forgive me. I want to be your friend, not your judge.

Lord, I ask that You to forgive me for having taken Your place as the judge of myself. I ask You to take out the bitter root, and wash me clean with Your blood. Please come into that place, filling it with Your Holy Spirit."

Section 3
Listen to EVERY negative emotion, and pray –

Every moment, every day, for the rest of your life!

The following are common questions people have expressed about their healing walk:

- How can I truly make peace with myself and come to love myself?
- How can I hear the voice of God so He can lead me in my healing?
- How can I take down The Wall inside me? (Chapter 9 of "I Will Give You Rest.").
- This healing thing is so complicated. How can I possibly get it right?
- How can I keep from losing the healing I have already attained?
- How can I know that the Lord has healed a bitter root?
- How do I know when there is a deeper root behind what just happened that triggered me?
- How can I know when I should be done praying?
- How can I possibly "count it all joy when I encounter various trials?"

Listening to every negative emotion is a very powerful practice that can provide the answers to these questions, and bring peace for the anxiety that results when emotions are stirred up.

Your negative emotions are a powerful tool that the Lord can use to direct your healing. He is in charge of your healing, truly wants you healed, and knows the path you need to follow to get healed. Therefore He puts you into situations that are divinely ordained to bring up the next issue He wants to work on. He will tell you about it by the negative feeling that comes up. It is like a dentist poking around in your mouth. When he touches a sore spot, you know it.

Your negative emotions are in fact God talking to you!

Therefore, your negative emotions are a powerful way that the Lord can lead you, all day every day. Then, you can truly "count it all joy," because the pain is going to lead to healing.

THE ASSIGNMENT

Pay Attention

Keep a pad of paper with you to write down every incident of a negative emotion, no matter how small.   Your response can be a short note or a long journal. It is your choice. If it is more convenient, you might use your cell phone to note for yourself the incident.

A major purpose of keeping a written list is so that if at the end of the day your paper is blank, you will know you haven't been listening. We all judge (and therefore have a negative emotion) many times every day. It is very easy to fall back into the old pattern of not listening if we aren't careful.

Pray over each item on your list

Be diligent to set aside time to get quiet and comfortable where there is a minimum of distractions. Look at each item on the list. Close your eyes and remember the recent incident that triggered the negative emotion.

Choose **a feeling word** to describe the feeling. Most negative emotions are signals that you have judged. If you need help choosing a feeling word, **see the attached list** of emotions. "**I feel like** she betrayed me," or "**I feel like** hitting him," are conclusions, not emotions. "I feel betrayed," or "I feel angry" are descriptions of the emotions. If you have not been used to paying attention to your emotions, naming them may take practice. The idea is to identify the signal coming up from inside, and to label it; so that you know what went wrong, and thus will know how to pray.

Then forgive whomever/whatever you have judged.
If your Treasure Inside is the one you have judged, ask him/her to forgive you.
- Ask the Lord to forgive you for the judgment,
- To remove the bitter root
- To cleanse that place with His blood
- To fill that place with His spirit.

Sample Prayers

I always hesitate to give sample prayers, because we need to be praying as Jesus leads, not in a rote prayer. You will find some suggestions in "How To Forgive" in a previous section of this Instruction Manual.

After you pray

Review the incident and see if there is peace. If there is peace, you are done. If not, there is more praying to be done. The further praying may have to do with the current event, or there may be an older, deeper root to be prayed about.

When you have peace, you are done. Peace means that the work the Lord wanted you to do right now is done. It does not necessarily mean that every bitter root with respect to that person or type of situation is gone. If there is more in there, in due season the Lord will bring it up and show you. See "Going Deeper" below.

Once you have prayed and have peace, then just go on and enjoy the day.

Continue Paying Attention
If at the end of any given day you have an almost blank piece of paper, this always means you haven't been listening. We all judge many times a day.

Making Friends With Yourself
If you have a history of judging yourself, once you begin to listen to your negative emotions, you may be astonished at how awful you are to yourself. In fact, you may find that almost every time that you experience a negative emotion, you have also judged yourself. Watch out for this.

A key to healing is to make friends with your Treasure Inside. This friendship, built on a growing trust, comes about by listening every time your Treasure Inside sends up a negative feeling. This is a bit like a parent with a child. If the child cries, a good parent will ask the child what is wrong, with the idea of correcting whatever is the problem. When a parent does this consistently, the child grows to trust the parent, knowing the parent has their best interest at heart.

The Role Of Positive Emotions
Also listen to your positive emotions, because they are also directional. They point you towards things that are good for you. Following them can lead to you having your legitimate needs met in legitimate ways ("I Will Give You Rest" pages 51, 175, 182).

It is not selfish to listen to your positive emotions. Of course, since the positive emotion was not pointing out sin, no prayer of forgiveness is necessary. Just enjoy the positive emotion, and perhaps thank the Lord for the good thing it is telling you about!

The Questions
What about the common questions posed at the beginning of this chapter? By letting the Lord lead you through your negative emotions, and forgiving and being forgiven (applying the blood of Jesus), you will find all these questions being answered.

You can't do it, but Jesus can - and wants to! Through this process you will be changed into the image of Jesus, step by step.

An Extra Bonus Of This Practice:
Listening to every negative emotion, recognizing I have judged, forgiving and being forgiven, is in fact the giving up the Lordship of my life, moment by moment, to the Lord Jesus. It causes me to become aware of my need for a Savior many times a day. This is a very good thing, and draws me closer to Him.

Going Deeper

Beyond what just happened today, the Lord wants to also heal you of past hurts. How do you find the old bitter roots? Sometimes they are obvious. But sometimes they are more hidden.

After you forgive and are forgiven of the present situation, if there is still not peace, this is an indication that the Lord is not done yet. Both He and your Treasure Inside know what else is ready to be revealed. The following practice can help you discover what is hidden from your conscious mind.

The following steps will enhance your ability to hear what is hidden:

1. Get quiet and comfortable. Relax. Close your eyes. Breathe deeply. If possible, be in a place with few distractions.
2. Invite the Lord to come and be with you and to lead you. Ask Him to protect you from the wiles of the enemy.
3. Focus your attention on your physical heart and the area around it. I find that placing my hand on my heart helps.
4. Ask your Treasure Inside your question. Turn your attention to your Treasure Inside, and thus to God who speaks there. If you seek to understand the reason for a negative feeling you recently had, ask your Treasure Inside to tell you about it. Because your Treasure Inside sent up the negative emotion, he or she initiated the conversation and has just been waiting for you to ask.
5. Be quiet. <u>Listen</u>. Don't try to make anything happen. If your mind begins to race, perhaps saying something like, "What a waste of time. You have a lot that you have to do," or any of its tactics to get back in control, simply go back to Step #3 again.
6. Take whatever comes up - a thought, a memory, a feeling, a scene (vision), a song, etc. Don't judge it, just accept it. Then focus on it. You may immediately know what it is telling you. If you don't, ask your Treasure Inside to tell you more, and listen again. It is very likely that the emotion you just had in the current event is similar to what you felt when the old event happened; and so it may be a clue as to the root the Lord wants to deal with.
7. When you are done, ask the Lord to help you fill you with appreciation. Feel the feeling. Count your blessings. Ending with a positive feeling brings you and your Treasure Inside closer together.

. . . and the peace of God, which surpasses all understanding, will guard your hearts and minds through Christ Jesus. Finally, brethren, whatever things are true, whatever things are noble, whatever things are just, whatever things are pure, whatever things are lovely, whatever things are of good report, if there is any virtue and if there is anything praiseworthy - meditate on these things (Philippians 4:7-8).

List Of Negative Emotions

If you have difficulty naming your negative emotions, I am providing a list that may help you to identify them.

Anger is a very common negative emotion. When you feel anger, you need to go deeper. Look below the anger, and you will find another emotion that is being expressed as anger. It is important to find the underlying emotion, because it is a clue as to what went wrong when you judged; and therefore helps you to know how to pray. Below is a list of emotions that often express themselves as anger.

Belittled	Fearful	Mad
Betrayed	Frustrated	Not heard
Controlled	Furious	Powerless
Cross	Grouchy	Small
Disvalued	Ignored	Threatened
Exasperated	Indignant	Unimportant
Fear	Insecure	

Other Negative Emotions

Abhorrence	Defiled	Gloomy
Agitated	Depressed	Gossipy
Aggravated;	Desolate	Grasping
Alarmed	Desperate	Greedy
Aloof	Despondent	Grieved
Annoyed	Different	Grim
Anxious	Dirty	Half-hearted
Apathetic	Disappointed	Hate
Apprehensive	Discontented	Helpless
Ashamed	Disgusted	Hesitant
Attacked	Dislike	Homesick
Aversion	Disdain	Hopeless
Baffled	Domineering	Hurt
Bewildered	Doomed	Impatient
Bitter	Dull	Inadequate
Blah	Edgy	Incapable
Boastful	Egotistical	Incompetent
Bored	Embarrassed	Indifferent
Callous	Envious	Inferior
Cautious	Exhausted	Inflexible
Confused	Fiendish	Inhibited
Conniving	Foolish	Insecure
Contempt	Forlorn	Insignificant
Cranky	Forgetful	Intimidated
Defeated	Friendless	Intolerant
Defensive	Fussy	Irritable

Isolated
Jealous
Lazy
Lethargic
Listless
Lonely
Lustful
Mangy
Martyred
Mean
Mediocre
Melancholy
Merciless
Meticulous
Miserly
Misjudged
Misunderstood
Morose
Mournful
Muddled
Mystified
Naked
Nauseated
Neglected
Nervous
Obstinate
Out of control
Out of place

Overcome
Overworked
Panicky
Paralyzed
Passive
Perplexed
Pooped
Pressured
Reluctant
Repulsed
Resentful
Resigned
Restless
Restrained
Ridiculous
Sad
Sarcastic
Scheming
Seductive
Self-conscious
Shabby
Shaky
Shy
Sick
Skeptical
Stubborn
Sulky
Suspicious

Tearful
Tempted
Tense
Terrified
Threatened
Timid
Tired
Traumatized
Troubled
Two-faced
Undone
Uncaring
Uncertain
Unconcerned
Uneasy
Un-loveable
Upset
Unglued
Unstable
Unsure
Unwanted
Uptight
Vulnerable
Weary
Wilted
Worried
Worthless

Positive Emotions

Admired
Affirmed
Alive
Ambitious
Amused
Appreciated
Approved
Astonished
Awed
Belonging
Blessed
Bold
Brave
Calm
Carefree
Cheerful
Comfortable
Compassionate
Confident
Considerate
Contented
Cooperative
Courageous
Creative
Curious
Delighted
Desire
Determined
Eager
Ecstasy
Efficient
Elated
Empowered
Encouraged
Energetic
Enjoyment
Enthusiastic
Euphoric
Excited
Expectant
Exuberant
Free
Friendly
Generous
Gentle
Glad
Gracious

Grateful
Happy
Helpful
Hopeful
Hospitable
Important
Impressed
Independent
Inspired
Interested
Irresistible
Joyful
Kind
Liked
Longing
Love
Loveable
Mellow
Merciful
Merry
Met
Open
Optimistic
Overjoyed
Patient
Peaceful
Pleasure
Reasonable
Relaxed
Romantic
Safe
Satisfaction
Secure
Self-assured
Sensible
Sensitive
Sensual
Sentimental
Serene
Serious
Soft
Sophisticated
Sure
Sympathetic
Talkative
Tender
Tenacious

Thankful
Thrilled
Tranquil
Transparent
Triumphant
Unbiased
Under-
standing
Understood
Validated
Valued
Vibrant
Yearning

Section 4
Applying It With Other Friends

- Meeting With Jesus

Why Meet With Others?

It can sometimes seem simpler and safer to do your healing alone. You may have been so wounded by others that meeting with others, and being vulnerable to them, may not be very appealing.

The simple answer to this question is that your healing journey works better in relationship with other people. A very powerful thing happens when people meet together and pray. For some reason, God chose to make it so. When others pray for you, your healing is more rapid. The whole New Testament is full of people in relationship. He refers to the Body of Christ as containing many members (for example 1 Corinthians 12:10-27). Whether you know it or not, you need others, and they need you.

The process of being set free from our bitter roots, and then Jesus coming into those places is the process of the Lord miraculously bringing forth life where there had been death. In John 11:43-44 there is the story about the Lord Jesus miraculously bringing Lazarus back to life. Then after Lazarus came out of the tomb, alive again, Jesus told the people: "Loose him, and let him go." For some reason, Jesus wanted the people to participate in the event by removing Lazarus' grave clothes. Likewise, sometimes He wants us to participate in the resurrection of our brothers and sisters in Christ.

> "Therefore confess your sins to each other and pray for each other so that you may be healed. The prayer of a righteous man is powerful and effective" (James 5:16 NIV).

If you are really serious about your healing, find a way to meet with others to apply the blood of Jesus to those places in you that need Him.

Who to Meet With

Ask the Lord who you should invite. Be clear to them about what you have in mind. If someone is not interested, accept that and find someone else who is excited about the idea. The Holy Spirit is the One who must open hearts to the Good News of transformation.

You may end up with just one other person, or several. That is OK.

Frequency of Meeting

I would suggest that you meet weekly. If you meet less often, you lose momentum, and close relationships do not develop.

Focus of the Meeting

Since the purpose of your meeting is to apply the blood of Jesus to the bitter roots, that is the place to start.

Always start your time together by meeting with Jesus. Make Him the focus of your meeting. Spend at least the first half of your time meeting with Him, and praying for one another.

Reserve your discussion time for the **end** of the meeting, if there is any time left over. You may find that you get so blessed in meeting with Jesus that you never get around to talking with each other. That is just fine. You will have done the healing part.

Picture this: if you were gathered in your home with a few friends, and Jesus actually physically walked into the room (as He did when He showed Thomas His wounds, John 20:27), who do you think you would all focus upon?

Think about that for a moment!

Then who do you think you would share your struggles with? Would you ignore Him and just talk to one another?

He may not physically show up to meet with you and your friends, but He is there, it you will pay attention.

> "For where two or there are gathered together in My name, I am there in the midst of them" (Matthew 18:20, NKJV).

This is a promise, and so you can count on it.

Therefore, the format of a meeting with Jesus should be to first recognize that He is there, and then act like it.

Tell Him your struggles and difficulties, in the presence of your friends.

Speak to Him, and not to your friends.

Then forgive and be forgiven as necessary, as He tells Peter **in the very next verse.**

> "Then Peter came to Him and said, 'Lord, how often shall my brother sin against me, and I forgive Him? Up to seven times?' Jesus said to him, 'I do not say to you, up to seven times, but up to seventy times seven" (Matthew 18:21-22 NKJV).

It is significant that Jesus brings up forgiving right after he mentions the value of gathering together. This likely means that the two should be linked together.

Your friends can help you with your prayers, praying for you as the Lord leads them (James 5:16 again).

You don't have to figure out how to conduct the meeting. Just let Jesus lead the way.

Confidentiality Is Necessary

It is important that what goes on in the prayer time remains confidential, unless the person gives permission to share their experience with others outside the group. People are also going to be inhibited in sharing their struggles when others are present, unless they know that it is safe to share their deepest secrets.

Preparation for this meeting with Jesus

It would be essential that each person is daily working on their own healing with the Lord. If not, they will have nothing to bring to the meeting, and they will likely receive very little from getting together.

Since the Lord is active in each person's life 24/7, He will lead and guide each of you all week long. Keep a list of what He brings up in your life during the week, including each negative emotion you experience. Bring your list to the meeting to pray about any unfinished business.

The reason for keeping a journal during the week is to remind you of what has been going on. Your journal also gives you your individual list to pray about on your own, as discussed elsewhere in this Instruction Manual. Jesus knows and did not forget, but you might.

Applying It With A Counselor/Prayer Minister

When You May Need Help

The Lord will be able to reveal to you or your friends most of your roots of bitterness. However, sometimes you need more help to find some of the deepest, most difficult roots. Sometimes you need the help of a person who has an anointing from the Lord and has experience praying with others. If that were not so, my type of counseling ministry would be unnecessary.

But where do you find someone who can help you with this? Of course, you are welcome to come and see me in Post Falls, Idaho (near Spokane, Washington). But this is often not feasible. So then how do you go about finding someone near you?

Be very careful in Choosing A Counselor/Prayer Minister!

The right person can be a great asset in your healing. The wrong person can cause you great damage and distress.

There are some counselors who apply the blood of Jesus to the bitter root causes. However, most counselors **do not.** Even most "Christian counselors" **do not.** If they do not, they will definitely do more harm than good. That omission is the rule, not the exception. Therefore, if you get a referral to a counselor, ask for one free session so that you can ask them about their approach. If the blood of Jesus is not their emphasis, don't go back.

A List of Counselors/Prayer Ministers

We do know of ministries in a few cities that could help you. There certainly may be more, but these are the ones we know about.

The reason there are so few on our list is because we are very particular about recommending ministries. We will only recommend people who we know use an approach similar to what I have written about in "I Will Give You Rest."

At the same time, these are all people who are completely independent from Edward Kurath and Divinely Designed. They have their own ministries, and we exercise no control over their practice, fees, licensure, or any other aspect of their ministries. Therefore, we make no guarantee about the outcome you will experience in praying with them. We recommend that you interview them so that you can decide for yourself if the person is a good match for you.

Because the list of counselors is dynamic it is not printed in this Workbook. To see the list of counselors, go to www.divinelydesigned.com. At the top of the Home Page, click on "Other Resources." Then scroll down and click on "Counselor Referrals."

Section 5
Group Leader's Guide

We want to affirm you in your personal journey of inner healing and in your desire to facilitate others in that journey using the "I Will Give You Rest" book, workbooks, and video materials. Be assured that the Lord will lead you on this journey, and we want to help to equip you to follow His leading as you reach out to others. He loves all of them and wants them to be set free.

For people to be transformed into the image of Jesus, the "head knowledge" obtained from the book and videos must be personally applied to one's life – a "spiritual process" that occurs through prayer.

Why Have A Group?

It is much more difficult for a person to apply this in isolation. Transformation is a daily process, and often people need the encouragement and accountability of other people. Without the support of a group, it is very difficult to persevere and to stay on track.

There are several reasons why working on our healing in a group enhances the process:

1. Scripture encourages us to gather together and pray for one another. There is an empowering dynamic that exists when we do this:
   a. "For where two or three are gathered together in My name, I am there in the midst of them" (Matthew 18:20, NKJV).
   b. "Therefore, confess your sins to one another, and pray for one another, so that you may be healed." (James 5:16, NAS).
2. Most of us need the encouragement of, and accountability to, other people to continue to diligently pray as we need to. Our healing is a process, and by ourselves it is too easy to let it fall by the wayside.
3. We can be blind to our own issues, and so we sometimes need the insight of others to help us see our own roots.
4. It is an encouragement to us to witness the healing of others in the group.

The purpose of this manual is to help you to facilitate an effective group where transformation can occur.

There needs to be two steps to the process.
1. **First,** the students need to become familiar with the Lord's way of healing. This is accomplished by first watching the videos and discussing them, and then using the book and Study Guide to further review and study the principles.
2. **Second,** the students need to apply what they have learned to their own lives. Meeting with other students to pray for each other is very helpful in accomplishing this.

The long term goal is that the students will be able to apply the blood of Jesus to their own lives for the rest of their lives. Some of them may also become inspired to begin to conduct their own groups in the future.

Schedule

Since the purpose of the group is to bring about healing, it helps the process if the students quickly reach a place where they can begin to pray for one another. Therefore, I would recommend that the **sequence** of chapters be altered to more quickly equip the group members to be able to pray for one another effectually.

Other Challenges:

There are some challenges that need to be overcome for people to truly receive healing in the meetings.

Usually the groups meet on weekday nights. This being the case, people have a limited amount of time and energy on any given night. The suggested schedule allows for a shorter meeting without compromising the effectiveness of each meeting.

There is a major mindset change between watching the video and discussing it (an intellectual process that occurs in **our head**), and listening to the Lord and praying (a spiritual process that occurs **inside us**). If an attempt is made to do both the teaching and prayer on the same night, I have found that it is very difficult for people to make this mindset change, and usually it is the prayer time that suffers.

The following suggested schedule also enhances the group prayer since people have time to digest a particular teaching and to apply it to their own lives for a week before they gather for the next prayer time.

In order for the prayer times to stay focused on their purpose, it needs to be clearly understood that when people come for the prayer time, that it is for prayer, not for study.

This schedule can also make the meetings more flexible: people who aren't ready to be vulnerable to a group can still come to the teaching nights only. Those who come to the prayer time have committed to the process, and know what to expect on the group prayer nights.

Suggested Pattern

- Watch a teaching video and then discuss the topic.
- During the following seven days, each person applies the teaching of the video to their own life, using the Study Aid as a guide.
- The next week, pray for one another in a small group.
- The next meeting after the prayer week, watch the next teaching video and then discuss the topic.

- Repeat this pattern of a watching a teaching video followed by a week of personal application and reflection in preparation for the prayer time.

You will note that for the first three weeks there are no prayer times interspersed. The reason for this is that the students need to get some basic information before they will be able to know how to pray in the fourth week.

One note of caution: Sometimes people tend to skip doing the Application Questions for Chapters 2, 3, 4 and 5 the week following each teaching, and to then cram them all in after the teaching of Chapter 5; because a prayer week is coming up. Try to warn them of this temptation, and encourage them to do the questions each week after a chapter is taught. The teachings will benefit them much more if they will do this.

Suggested Schedule

Week	Agenda	Assignment
1	Watch Chapters 2 & 3	Discuss what to expect in the group
		Study Guide questions
		Begin Life History Form
2.	Watch Chapter 4	Study Guide questions
3	Watch Chapter 5	Study Guide questions
		How to Forgive
4.	Prayer	
5.	Watch Chapter 11	Study Guide questions
		Listen to Every Negative Emotion
6.	Prayer	
7.	Watch Chapter 9	Study Guide questions
8.	Prayer	
9.	Watch Chapter 7	Study Guide questions
10.	Prayer	
11.	Watch Chapter 10	Study Guide questions
12.	Prayer	
13.	Watch Chapters 12 & 13	Study Guide questions
		Read Chapter 16 (there is no video)
14.	Prayer	
15.	Watch Chapter 6	Study Guide questions
	Discuss Chapter 16	
16.	Prayer	
17.	Watch Chapters 14 & 15	Study Guide questions
		People pray about being prayed for
		Next prayer time, as discussed in Chapter 15.
18.	Prayer – try Inner Child Prayer	
19.	Watch Chapters 8 & 18	Study Guide questions
20.	Prayer	
21.	Watch Chapter 17 and discuss **"what next?"**	

There are several possibilities for **"What next?"**
- Continue to meet and pray for each other – our transformation is a lifelong process, and the group can facilitate this.
- Start over by adding new students and hopefully using current members as prayer group leaders.
- Current prayer group participants start their own new groups.

<u>Suggestions for Conducting Prayer Group Meetings</u>

In addition to the teaching segment, we are providing this "how-to" guide to address topics related to facilitating a prayer group that desires to apply the teachings of the "I Will Give You Rest."

> "Therefore, confess your sins to one another, and pray for one another, so that you may be healed. The effective prayer of a righteous man can accomplish much" (James 5:16 NAS).

Encouragement

The first thing we would like you to remember is that the Lord is the healer. You as the facilitator are primarily along for the ride. You do have a part to play; but as long as the focus is on Jesus and His presence, and the environment is safe, the group will become successful. Therefore, please do not become anxious about the guidelines we will be suggesting.

I. Organization of the Prayer Group

Formation: There is no set rule as to how group members should be chosen. Pray about it and follow the Lord's leading. The Lord knows each person intimately, and He knows the group dynamic He wants to promote. These are things we probably can't know. For instance, sometimes couples should be split up, and sometimes not. Sometimes people of the same sex should be in the same group, and sometimes not. Sometimes good friends should be in separate groups, and sometimes not. Sometimes people of the same generation should be together, and sometimes not.

One guideline that should probably be followed is that people who are known to be antagonistic towards each other should not be in the same group. Otherwise their hostility will delay or eliminate the possibility of safety developing in the group. For example, a married couple who are in strife with each other should be in separate groups.

Attendance: Generally, the prayer group membership should be permanent. Movement of people into or out of the group once it has begun to function interferes with the group dynamic and sense of safety, and this could delay the maturation and effectiveness of the group. Each person needs to commit to doing their best to come every time the group meets. Obviously, unforeseen and sporadic problems need to be understood, and could be an opportunity for the other group members to pray for the absent one. If a person does not feel that he or she can make this commitment to the group, he or she can still come to the teaching weeks, but should not be a member of a prayer group. As a prayer group facilitator, if you have to miss a prayer group meeting, try to identify another group member who can facilitate that meeting.   Plan ahead if possible.

Size: One group should generally be no more than eight people. If the group gets bigger than this, people may be reluctant to share. In addition, more people can limit the amount of prayer time each person can receive. Divide in smaller groups if you have more than eight.

Leader: Each group should have a Facilitator who is familiar with the teachings, and thus the assignments and how to pray. If the first time through the teachings you are the only person who knows the material well enough to be able to lead a prayer group, then the first time you do the group teaching you should limit the prayer time to one group, which you will facilitate. Hopefully, after the first time through the teachings and prayer time, some other members of the prayer group will also be able, and motivated, to facilitate in the future.

Confidentiality: Everything shared in the group needs to be confidential. Every group member needs to agree to this.

The only exception would be if spouses are in separate groups. In this situation, they can share their experiences in their own group with each other, IF the other <u>can be trusted</u> not to tell other people the confidential information. If the spouse cannot be trusted, then he or she must not share confidential information. The reason for this exception is that it would not be a good thing if participation in the prayer group would build a wall between husband and wife.

II. Safety in the Prayer Group
The foundation of a prayer group is SAFETY. If the group is a safe place, and Jesus is the focus, the group will become successful. Lack of safety, respect, love, and concern is what wounded most people. Because of prior unsafe experiences, many have developed automatic defenses that will rise up when they sense a lack of safety. Feeling safe is the only way that people will reach the place where they are willing to share the deep secrets of their lives.

Down deep, every human desires to be heard and respected, and their Treasure Inside craves to have deep relationships with other people. The fact that a person has decided to participate in the prayer group says that he or she consciously wants healing. However, our defense mechanisms are subconscious, and we don't have conscious control over their operation. Those who have been more deeply wounded may take longer to begin to share at a deep level.

Experiencing and observing love and acceptance being displayed in the group is the only way to keep the defense mechanisms from triggering a shut down. As the group matures and healing occurs, the defense mechanisms will be eliminated. Then the person will be able to be open whenever he or she senses a safe person, or to stay private when safety is not present.

As the Facilitator, realize that the sense of trust and safety takes time to develop. Be patient with others and yourself. To begin with, most of the group members either don't know each other, or have probably never experienced that depth of relationship with other people. They first need to become comfortable with the others in the prayer group.

Consider being the first one to share, to break the ice. Your application of the teachings to your own life will model for others what the homework was about, and how to pray about it in the group. Seeing that you are a safe and nonjudgmental person, yet a sinner like they are, will encourage them to risk sharing their own experience and to be prayed for.

Also be aware that people in our culture are not accustomed to sharing their feelings and problems with others in a group. This cultural hurdle is one reason why small groups in American churches have not been very successful. This is also one reason why people feel more comfortable when they are in their head than sharing from deep inside. Because of this, as the Facilitator, from time to time you may need to bring the group back to praying. One of the most effective ways of doing that is to ask them to become quiet and to then listen inside.

III. Sharing/Praying in the Prayer Group

Preparing to Pray: Be sure your group members understand that the sharing/praying time is for sharing struggles and for praying – for communing in the spirit realm, with the Lord and with your Treasures Inside. The prayer time is for applying to your lives what was taught the previous weeks. The teaching week is the place to ask questions and to discuss the lessons.

Unless this distinction is made clear and adhered to, the prayer times can easily become times of visiting and discussion and giving of advice – of communing head to head. If the time is spent in your heads, no healing will occur. From time to time you, as the facilitator, may need to bring the group back to reflection if they get into their heads in this way. In our culture we tend to feel uncomfortable with quiet moments, and tend to fill the quiet with words.

This distinction is why we recommend that alternate weeks be dedicated to prayer. Without this clear separation, it is quite likely that the group will not spend much time actually praying. This way the prayer group members come to the prayer time prepared and knowing what the focus will be.

To prepare for prayer, start out with a time for quieting that will help transition members from the cares of the day to focusing inside on the Holy Spirit. Times of quiet are important. If a person is listening for the voice of the Lord, or their Treasure Inside, there needs to be quiet. They may have to close their eyes and sit for awhile to hear what is coming up from inside. Open eyes can bring outside stimulation that pops a person back into their head. Words spoken at the wrong time can do this same thing. The only way to know when it is appropriate to speak is to listen to the Holy Spirit, Who is directing the prayer time. Encourage everyone to let quiet times occur. It is an essential part of listening, because the healing that the Lord wants to bring about occurs inside.

Sharing/praying: Encourage everyone to come to the prayer meeting with an open mind rather than an agenda. That way the Lord can be free to do whatever He wants to accomplish. We can't know what that is ahead of time.

One good way to start the prayer time that opens the door for the Lord and his agenda is to ask people to take turns telling Jesus one thing they like about Him. This can get the ball rolling in a spirit of praise.

Another way to pray is to simply be quiet and wait for the Lord to speak to someone. Hopefully, the group members will have been spending the previous week prayerfully applying the prior teaching to their own lives, and the Lord may have greatly stirred certain people to share. Those people will usually be the place to start. If nobody jumps out, then you might have each person read one event from their list of issues that came up during the prior week, and pray with them.

There are many ways to pray, and the group needs to be open and available to proceeding as the Lord leads. This may be dynamic and sometimes maybe even surprising. It is important that the Facilitator not come to the meeting with a fixed agenda, but rather come with a listening ear. It is not possible to know ahead of time what the Lord has been doing in the lives of the individuals between prayer meetings. Take what the Lord presents.

When the group is new, respect those who do not yet feel free to share. They may have wounds that make them very cautious. As they grow in their sense of safety, they will usually eventually begin to share. It they don't ever get around to sharing, this is likely a perfect thing to pray with them about. If they never get around to bringing their issues to the group, they will not get prayer, and probably not be healed.

Each person is different. If an individual doesn't ever get around to sharing, you may eventually need to draw them out. Likewise, try not to let the same one or two people dominate every meeting. If this tends to happen, then these people are not being empathetic with others in the group. This is likely a sign of a wound in them. Again, this may be a perfect thing to pray with them about.

Each person should work at becoming an active listener. People know when they are being heard, and that can be a very healing thing for them. Some people have never been listened to or understood.

Celebrate when a person has a breakthrough. Observing one member's breakthrough can be enormously encouraging to other members.

On the other hand, when a member is discouraged, first listen to him or her. Then help the person to process this.

Jesus is Present: If Jesus was physically in the room with the group, His presence would undoubtedly dominate the attention of the members; and they would likely spend most of their time <u>addressing Him directly</u>. Though He is not present physically, if we invite Him to be there, He promises to be with us.*" For where two or three are gathered together in My name, I am there in the midst of them"* (Matthew 18:20, NKJV). Therefore, you can cultivate that awareness, and <u>encourage people to address Jesus directly and not so much each other</u> by saying, "Can you tell Jesus that?", or "What is Jesus doing?"

One goal that is very productive for inner healing is to eventually move to the type of prayer discussed in Chapter 15 of my book. Because of the trust required between a person and his or her Treasure Inside, it may take some time for this to begin to work. Be patient. Try it from time to time with willing members. When a person is able to see the Lord and hear what He is doing and saying, miraculous things happen.

Whenever a person is praying, it is helpful if he or she will speak slowly and loudly enough so that others can know what they are praying, or what the Lord is showing them. This is especially true with Chapter 15 type prayer. If a person is seeing the Lord, it will help the group if the one seeing the vision will verbalize what is going on as it is happening.

If at any time other group members sense something, or see something in the spiritual realm, it is important that he or she be sensitive as to what to share with the group, and when.

Summary
Therefore, the primary assignment for the Facilitator is to promote an environment where James 5:16 can happen. Each group member needs to be encouraged to personally interact directly with the Lord, to receive healing from Him; and to "pray for one another."

IV. Follow through
The most straightforward assignment for members is to <u>listen to every negative emotion and pray</u> as best they can (see the assignment to do this in the Instruction Manual). After the teaching of Chapter 11 on emotions, everyone should be doing this constantly. Then the members should bring their list of experiences to the group meeting, and have the group pray about anything for which they were not able to get to a place of peace.

It is very important that the members apply the teachings to their own lives between prayer meetings. Applying the blood of Jesus to their own lives is the only thing that will bring healing to them.

In addition, one of the objectives of the prayer group and the assignments is to prepare people to be able to personally process their own issues with the Lord outside the group. The group will likely not be there for the rest of their lives, but they will need the Lord to be their healer for the rest of their days on this earth.

V. Facilitator Encouragement

It will take a load off your shoulders if you can truly come to realize that the Lord is in charge. <u>You can't make any healing happen</u>. Know that the Lord Jesus Christ is heavily invested in each person's life, and He is the only One that can bring healing to them. So just be listening to His leading and follow Him. Hopefully, each person in the group will be doing this, and the Lord will fill in the gaps by directing them. Accept that in the Kingdom of God, everybody is of equal importance and "rank." He loves each person equally, and has a plan for each one's life.

At the same time, He has given each person unique gifts. As time goes by, it will become evident to the group – what gifts and talents God has placed in each person's Treasure Inside. Some people have no idea that they have gifts, or what are those gifts. Part of the journey of healing is for each person to get to know and to love their own Treasure Inside, and to celebrate who God made them to be. The other group members may have to help them to identify and embrace and celebrate those gifts and talents.

At your first meeting, discuss with each other the content of this section. It is very important that people know what to expect from the group, and what they can contribute to it.

The Life History Form that follows can be a very useful tool in your healing. It's purpose is to help you to explore the details of your life, so that you can begin to understand more clearly your roots. The problems that we currently experience have their origin in our past. Please do not view the Form as a "hoop to jump through." Take your time, and ask the Lord to be with you and to give you understanding as you complete it.

LIFE HISTORY FORM

Counselor: Edward Kurath **P.O. Box 7501** **Golden, Colorado 80403**	**Divinely Designed** **Phone: (208) 755-9206** **e-mail: edkurath@divinelydesigned.com**

THIS FORM HAS TWO VERY IMPORTANT PURPOSES:

1. It can give a comprehensive picture of your background. By reading this completed form, your counselor (if you have one) can obtain information that would otherwise have to be explored during your valuable counseling time
2. The process of filling this out carefully can be very valuable to you. The form asks questions about yourself that perhaps you have not previously explored, and so completing it can help prepare your heart for the work the Lord wants to do for you.

Please prayerfully and carefully complete the form as fully and accurately as you can by yourself so that you can receive the maximum benefit that it can afford. If a question is too difficult or too painful to answer, you certainly may leave it blank. Your counselor (if you have one) will keep this information strictly confidential, and the information is not available to anyone without your written permission. (Please note that a child or client who cannot read and write may be asked the questions by an adult and the person's answers written for them. Information unknown to the child may be entered by an adult.

Please only use a pen when completing this form.   Today's Date_____

Name_____By what name would you like to be called?_____
        First   Middle   Last   _____

e-mail address_____ Phone_____ Date of Birth_____

Street Address_____

City_____State/Prov._____ May we call you at work? ☐ Yes   ☐ No

Country_____Zip/Postal Code_____ Work Phone_____

Emergency Contact Person (other than spouse)_____ Relationship_____

Street Address_____ Phone (Home)_____

City_____ State/Prov._____ Phone (Work)_____

Country_____ Zip/Postal Code_____

Have you been in military service? ☐ Yes   ☐ No If yes, branch of service and dates_____

Religion/Denomination_____ Place of worship_____
Worship attendance: ☐ Regular   ☐ Occasional   ☐ Not at all

How I learned about or was referred to Ed Kurath's counseling:_____
How strongly do you want help for your problems? ☐ Very much   ☐ Moderately   ☐ Could do without

Prior counseling received:

	Psychiatrist (MD)	Psychologist (PhD)	Psychotherapist	Lay Counselor	Pastoral
Type of counseling					
Number of hours					

Friends important to you:_____

NEED FOR COUNSELING

State in your own words the nature of your concern, and/or what you would like to see happen as a result of the counseling..

If your problem is something that you think happens too often, state approximately how often it occurs, how long it lasts and any other information you feel might be helpful in understanding your problem.

If your problem concerns something not happening as often as you would like, state what you would like to see happen more often, how often you think it should occur, etc.

If you have had previous counseling for this problem, state with whom and describe the outcome

YOUR DESIRES

How do you hope to use your healing to bless others?

BEGINNINGS
Place a check mark in each box that applies to you or write the facts as they pertain to each item:

Place of Birth: _____ Weight at Birth: _____pounds _____ounces

I was born: ☐ on time   ☐ late: How late? _____   ☐ premature: How premature?_____

☐ I was delivered Cesarean Section

☐ I was a wanted baby. How do you know?_____

☐ Birth mother and natural father were <u>not</u> married to each other before my conception.

☐ Birth mother and natural father were <u>not</u> happily married during my time in the womb.

☐ Natural father was gone much of the time while I was in the womb.

☐ Medications or forceps had to be used for my delivery.

☐ Birth mother and /or natural father were grieving the loss or potential loss of a loved one during my womb life

☐ Birth mother had a difficult previous pregnancy.

☐ Birth mother had a difficult pregnancy with me. What made it difficult?_____

☐ Birth mother and natural father were struggling with difficulties of life while I was in the womb. If yes, what were they?

What is the story your family tells about your coming into the world?

What significant events occurred in your early childhood?

List the number of "moves" you made in your first 18 years of life.

Age	Moved From	Moved To	Reason

HEALTH INFORMATION

Your present height: _____   weight: _____

List the number of hospitalizations or serious injuries you experienced in your first 18 years.

Incident:	Age:	Reaction & Present Effects:

HEALTH INFORMATION (continued)

Does any of your health history or experiences relate to your present problem?

List all prescription and non-prescription drugs you now take (include dosage):

When was the last time you felt well, both physically and emotionally, for a fair amount of time and why?

Menstrual History

Age of first period:_____ Were you informed, or did it come as a shock?
.

How did others respond to you?

Are you regular? ☐Yes ☐No Duration:_____ Do you have pain?. ☐Yes ☐No
Do your periods affect your moods? ☐Yes ☐No If so, how?

EDUCATIONAL HISTORY (List from most recent to oldest)

School/College/University	Major/Degree	Date Received:

Were you ever bullied or given a nickname? ☐Yes ☐No If yes, by whom and why?

Do you make friends easily? ☐Yes ☐No Do you keep them?

EMPLOYMENT HISTORY (List from most recent to oldest)

Age	Job	Type of work	Reason for Leaving

EMPLOYMENT (continued)

Do you enjoy your present job? ☐Yes ☐No Please explain further:

How much money do you and your spouse earn?_____Are you satisfied? ☐ Yes ☐ No

What are your ambitions and aspirations?

SEX INFORMATION

What was the attitude towards sex in the home in which you grew-up? How was it discussed or instructed?

At what age did you derive your knowledge of sex? _____ How did you learn?

When did you become aware of your sexual impulses? What happened?

Did someone ever touch you inappropriately in a sexual way? ☐Yes ☐ No If yes, please explain:

Did you ever have any anxieties, or guilt feelings, or trauma arising out of:

- Masturbation? ☐Yes ☐No If yes, please explain:

- Sexual Experience with the opposite sex? ☐Yes ☐ No If yes, please explain:

- Sexual Experience with the same sex (homosexuality)? ☐Yes ☐ No If yes, please explain:

Are there any questions, concerns and/or events you have about sex, sexual experiences and/or sexual identity past/present or future?

FAMILY DATA

List all of your brothers and sisters from oldest to youngest, including yourself. Please list in birth order, including any miscarriages, or abortions of which you are aware?

Name	Sex	Age	Marital Status	Job	Brief Description of Their Personality

What was your relationship with your brothers and sisters in the past? Explain why.

What is your present relationship with your brothers and sisters? Explain why.

Which brother or sister is most like you, and in what respect?

Which brother or sister is most different from you, and in what respect?

Who played together and why?

Have you ever lived with anyone other than your parents? ☐Yes ☐ No

If yes, how old were you? _____   For how long? _____

With whom did you live?

How would you describe the home atmosphere in which you grew-up?

Were you able to confide in your parents? ☐Yes ☐No   Why or why not?

Has anyone (parents, relatives, friends) ever interfered in your marriage, occupation, or other aspects of your personal life? ☐ Yes ☐ No   If yes, in what ways?

List any fearful or distressing experiences not previously mentioned:

DESCRIBE YOUR PARENTS
Answers on this page describe the mother and father who took primary responsibility for rearing you. If either person is other than your biological (birth) parent, **please copy these description pages**, complete them for your biological parent/s and attach that page to the back of this life history

FATHER's Name:	Current age:	**MOTHER's** Name:	Current age:
Occupation before retiring			
If deceased, what was the cause of death and their age?			
What was your age then?			
Personality			
Values			
Kind of home environment he/she provided			
Relationship to each other			
Was in charge - real head of house			

(Continued)	**FATHER**	**MOTHER**
Relationship to the children		
How he/she showed Love		
Ambition for the Children		
Describe your ability to confide in him/her		
Form of punishment he/she used		
As a child, what I liked about him/her		
As a child, what I disliked about him/her		
His/her favorite child and why		

(Continued)	FATHER	MOTHER
	Child most like him/her	
	Child most different from him/her	
	Attitude towards sex	
	Had a problem with addictions or immorality	

PARENTING STYLE IN YOUR FAMILY OF ORIGIN

For each issue, please circle the number which best describes your opinion of the home in which you grew-up.

	Too Permissive	Permissive	Average	Strict	Too Strict
Church attendance	5	4	3	2	
Clothing	5	4	3	2	1
Computer use	5	4	3	2	1
Dating	5	4	3	2	1
Drinking alcohol	5	4	3	2	1
Free will	5	4	3	2	1
Home chores	5	4	3	2	1
Literature	5	4	3	2	1
Movies	5	4	3	2	1
Music	5	4	3	2	1
School work	5	4	3	2	1
Sex	5	4	3	2	1
Smoking	5	4	3	2	1
Television	5	4	3	2	1

MARITAL INFORMATION

	Name of Spouse	Length of Engagement	Age When Married		Length of Marriage	Reason Why It Ended	# Children from that Marriage
			You	Spouse			
1st Marriage							
2nd Marriage							
3rd Marriage							
4th Marriage							

PRESENT MARRIAGE   Anniversary Date: _____

What I liked the first few years:

What my spouse liked the first few years:

.

What I disliked the first few years:

What my spouse disliked the first few years:

What I liked/disliked in the last few months:

What my spouse liked/disliked in the last few months:

Place the letter "C" or "I" in each blank below as it applies to your present marriage.
C = Most Compatible   I = Incompatible

_____ value system	_____ commitment to God	_____ devotion to spouse	_____
_____ Intellect	_____ sleep requirements	_____ financial planning	_____ child discipline
_____ energy level	_____ food appetite	_____ spending money	_____ devotion to work
_____ social time	_____ exercise needs	_____ parenting style	_____ household duties
_____ Planning	_____ sexual needs	_____ recreational interests	_____ in-law relationships
_____ Goals	_____ need for touch	_____ educational preparation	_____ hobbies
_____ Neatness	_____ need for time alone	_____ sensitivity to feelings	_____ other _____
_____ Friends	_____ conversation	_____ spiritual growth	_____ other _____

Give three specific examples of those things you would like to see your spouse do more often (eg. take out the garbage, bring you a cup of coffee, spend more time with you, etc.)

    1.
    2.
    3.

Give three specific examples of those things you would like to see your spouse stop doing (three particular things that irritate you).

    1.
    2.
    3.

List the names of **your children**, from oldest to youngest. State if any of these children are from previous marriages, or adopted. Also, in order of birth include any miscarriages or abortions. Include step-children.

First Name	Sex	Age	Marital Status	Job	Brief Description of Personality

PREVIOUS MARRIAGE(S) (If you have more than one prior marriage, turn sheet over and describe).

What I liked about them:

What I disliked about them:

What my previous spouse liked about me:

What my previous spouse disliked about me:

What ended the relationship?

On the following chart, please place a check mark beside each listed item as it applies to yourself (S) or other people in your Family of Origin (F).

On the following charts, please place a check mark beside each listed item as it applies to yourself (S) or other people in your Family of Origin (F).

S	F	
		inadequate
		anemia
		allergies
		lonely
		perfectionist
		generous
		dependent
		unworthy
		constipation
		bulimia
		obesity
		controlling
		bedwetting
		stammering
		forgetful
		headaches
		insomnia
		voice changes
		blood diseases
		doubts
		sinus problems
		depression
		feel tense
		cold sores
		difficult to pray
		low energy
		fear God
		verbal abuse
		arthritis
		feel invisible
		diabetes
		infertility
		mental illness
		dread vacations
		poverty

S	F	
		jaundice
		abortions
		asthma
		flee worship
		fear failure
		ambitious
		pleaser
		diarrhea
		underweight
		secretive
		body image worry
		moody
		masturbation
		nail biting
		intelligent
		double vision
		suggestible
		daydream
		hearing problems
		lost interest
		autism
		fatigue
		stomach trouble
		nightmares
		low energy
		easily annoyed
		feel inferior
		emotional abuse
		bitter
		physical abuse
		brain injury
		learning disability
		dread weekends
		dread holidays
		AIDS

S	F	
		alcoholism
		smoker
		shyness
		fantasy
		drug abuse
		gambling
		obsessive
		unable to relax
		anorexia
		compulsive
		cravings
		sexual addiction
		venereal disease
		panic attacks
		gifted [arts]
		TMJ
		homosexuality
		hear voices
		time conscious
		worry
		grief
		heart disease
		feel panic
		sexual problems
		frustration
		fear success
		difficulty deciding
		mental retardation
		bullied as child
		skin diseases
		sees life as good
		sees life as bad
		not listened to
		happy childhood
		sickle cell anemia

S	F	
		guilt feelings
		miscarriages
		fear of knives
		wish born another time
		thumb sucking
		DES baby
		dislike confrontation
		difficulty deciding
		peacemaker
		angry
		insecurity
		pornography
		bladder infections
		flashbacks
		dizziness
		blurred vision
		strange sensations
		convulsions / seizures
		shaking/tremors
		scars
		cancer
		kidney problems
		paralysis
		sees God as distant
		bad home conditions
		martyr
		spiritual abuse
		fear travel
		lack common sense
		narcolepsy
		can't express feelings
		flooded by feelings
		unhappy childhood
		tuberculosis
		can't keep friends

S	F	
		blood pressure problems
		P.M.S.
		suicidal thoughts
		blasphemous thoughts
		suicide
		feel ripped off
		financial problems
		rheumatic fever
		excessive exercise
		arrested for crime
		lustful thoughts
		hepatitis [A][B]
		bowel disturbances
		sleepwalking
		unexplained muscle pain
		accused of lying
		fibromyalgia
		uneven achievement in school
		thyroid problems
		orthopedic problems
		breathing problems
		liver problems
		fear going to hell
		poor work performance
		sees God as harsh
		difficult to read Bible
		unable to hold boundaries
		bad reaction to anesthetics
		hard to tell right from wrong
		difficulty deciding what to wear
		fear losing mind
		fear will hurt others
		fear terminal illness
		see moving shadows
		can't make friends

SPIRITUAL EXPERIENCES

Please place a check mark beside each item in which you or your family members have participated. Key: S = self , F = family

S	F		S	F		S	F	
		Islam			Masons (Freemasonry)			astral-projection
		Wicca			Christian Science			astrology
		Bahaism			Children of God			automatic writing
		EST			Church of the Living Word			black magic/ white magic
		Echkankar			Cult of Diana			blood pacts
		Father Divine			Herbert W. Armstrong			clairvoyance
		Hare Krishna			(Radio Church of God)			dowsing (water witching)
		Hinduism			Jehovah Witness			fetishism
		Science of Creative Intelligence			Scientology			fortune telling
		Rosicrucian			Mormonism			ghosts
		Roy Masters			New Age			healing magnetism
		Science of the Mind			Swedenborgianism			hypnosis
		Silva Mind Control						incubi or succubae (sex spirits)
		Theosophical Society			The Way International			magic charming
		Transcendental Meditation			Unification Church			materialization
		Yoga			Unitarianism			mental suggestions
		Zen Buddhism			Unity			ouija board
		Satanism			Witchcraft			palm reading
		Other:			Other: _____			pendulum &rod
		Other: _____			Other: _____			spells
								reading tea leaves, etc.
								séance
								tarot cards
								telekinesis (i.e., table lifting)
								telepathy
								trance speaking
								visionary dreams
								drugs

How have any of the items you checked affected your life?

SELF-DESCRIPTION

In what situations do you lose control?

In what situations do you maintain self-control?

How do you believe you would be described by:

- Your spouse:

- Your best friend:

- Your worst enemy (even if you don't really have one):

How would you describe yourself?

COMPLETE THE FOLLOWING SENTENCES

1) As a child, I . . .

2) For me, school was . . .

3) My childhood fears were . . .

4) My childhood ambitions were . . .

5) My role in my group of friends was . . .

6) The significant events in my physical and sexual development were . . .

7) The significant events in my social development were . . .

8) The most important values in my family were . . .

9) What stands out the most for me about my family life is . . .

10) My parents' relationship to each other was . . .

11) My brother' and sister' relationships to Dad were . . .

12) My brother' and sister' relationships to Mother were . . .

Resources & Contact Information:

Books by Edward Kurath:
- Exceeding Great and Precious Promises
- I Will Give You Rest
- I Will Give You Rest Devotional Version
- Workbook for I Will Give You Rest

Ways to buy books:
- Online:www.divinelydesigned.com
- Amazon.com
- By Phone: (208) 755-9206
- By Mail: Edward Kurath
    - Divinely Designed
    - PO Box 7501
    - Golden, Colorado 80403 USA

Counseling and Seminars
- Information online at: www. divinelydesigned.com
- E-mail:edkurath @divinelydesigned.com
- Phone: (208) 755-9206

Free Information
- Many chapters of I Will Give You Rest online
- Chapters of I Will Give You Rest in audio online
- Free PDF download of this Workbook available on the website
- Many chapters of Exceedingly Great and Precious Promises online
- Articles and other resources of interest